Guided Journal

A Place For All of Your Wildest Dreams, World-Changing Plans and Genius Ideas!

Lisa Goich

A GIRL ON THE GO BOOK
ISBN: 978-1-7354452-0-5
A Girl On The Go Guided Journal

Cover and internal design by Rose Audette
Illustrations from Shutterstock.com

A Girl On The Go
Los Angeles
agirlonthego.com
Published in the United States of America
1 2 3 4 5 6 7 8 9 10

This Book Is Dedicated To

You

Introduction

Hi. I'm Lisa and I'm A Girl On The Go!

I'm so happy to have you here, with pen in hand, ready to chart your life within these pages. I've been journaling since I was in elementary school. My journals were filled with poems, heartache, crushes, love letters, challenges, goals and dreams. When I'd have a problem I was having trouble solving, I'd always turn to my journal to work it out. There was something about putting things down on paper that always gave me perspective, and made the drama not so dramatic anymore. All these years later, I still use my journal to work through my issues of the day. I use it to celebrate my wins, to tackle my challenges, and to organize my thoughts and tasks to free my mind and make room for more fabulous, creative ideas.

I created prompts and exercises for this journal that I thought would help you as you travel down your own life path. Feel free to jump around - there is no formal start or end point. And if a prompt makes you think of something else you'd like to write about, create your own exercises!

If you run out of pages, get a blank journal to continue your writing.

This book is about you and for you. When you're finished filling its pages, tuck it in a safe place to read again at a future date. Trust me, it'll make for really, really great reading down the line!

Thank you for being a part of the A Girl On The Go community! I'm so happy to have you here. I hope you'll subscribe to our website for more prompts, activities, workshops and future books!

Here we GOOOOOOOOO!

Love,

Lisa

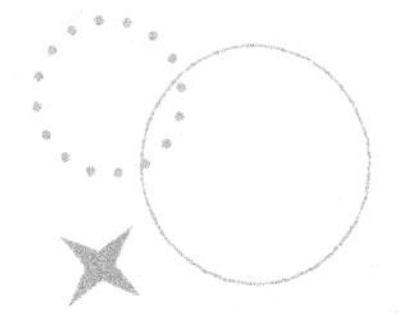

YOU
GO
GIRL

A Girl On The Go Is...

Adventurous

She welcomes new challenges and experiences.

Fearless

She doesn't let anything stand in her way.

Curious

She is full of wonder and loves to learn.

Inspired

She finds ideas in all that she sees and hears.

Driven

She keeps going regardless of what obstacles stand in her way.

Kind

She knows that living with kindness is good for the heart.

Giving

She values charity and giving to others.

Humble

She knows that modesty shines brighter than vanity.

I am...

Frida Khalo

Five famous women I admire and why...

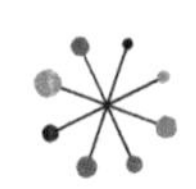

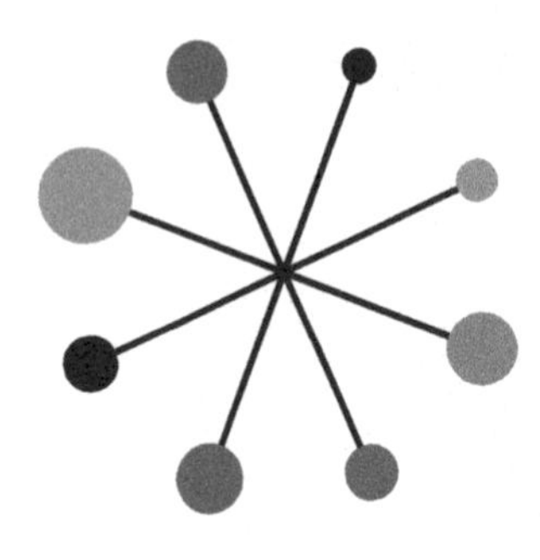

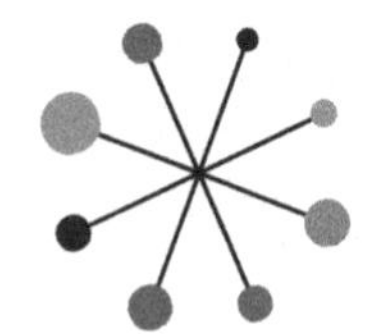

The greatest influence in my life has been...

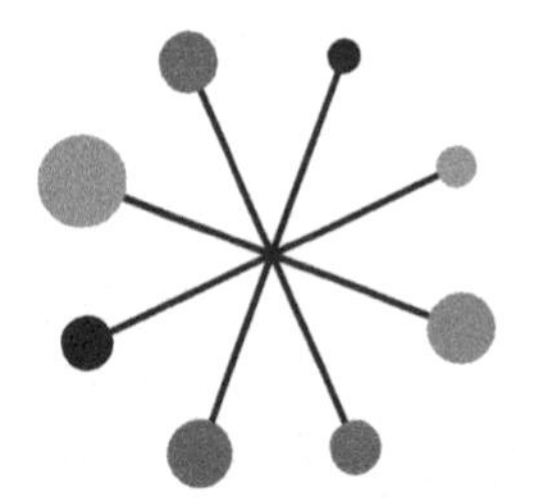

My best feature is...

The #1 thing I love about myself...

Things I do pretty awesomely...

I could be better at...

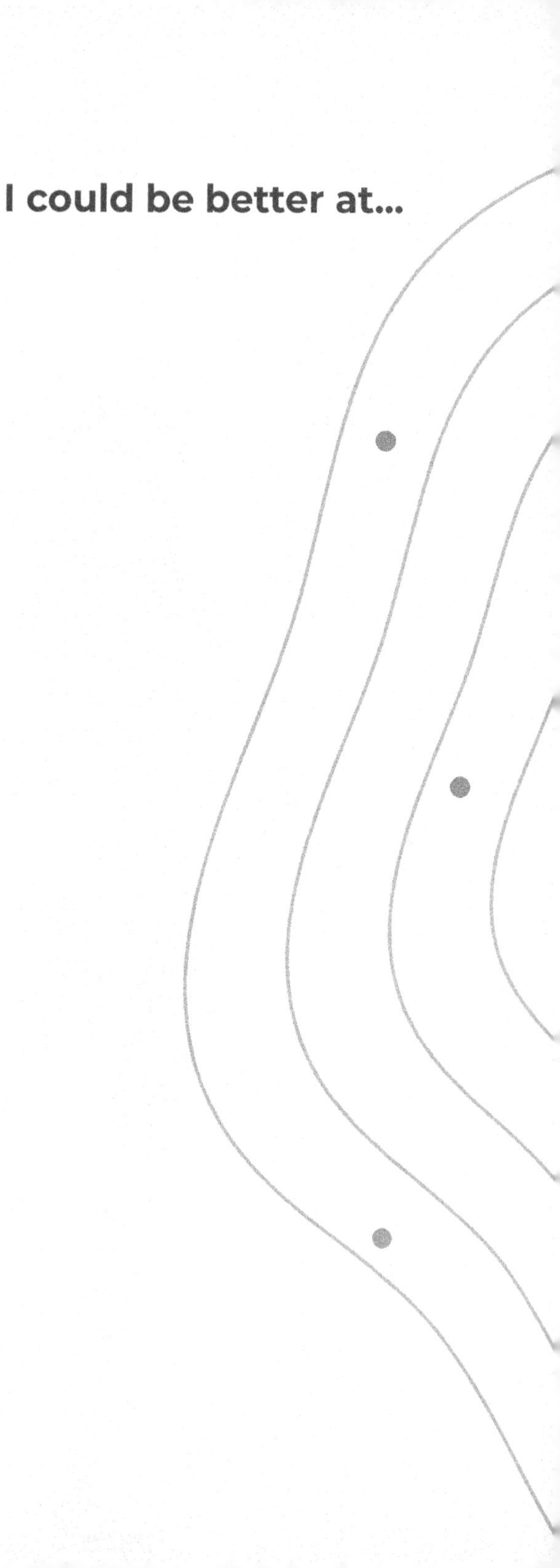

NEVER
doubt
YOUR
Greatness

My BFF is...

We have been friends since...

We both love...

We equally hate...

A secret we share between us...

I love her/him/them because...

Things I look for in a friend...

When I’m 25 I will...

When I'm 45 I will...

When I'm 85 I will...

Today I will...

I pledge to...

I dream of...

Some day I will...

My absolute best day ever was...

I’ve got big plans...

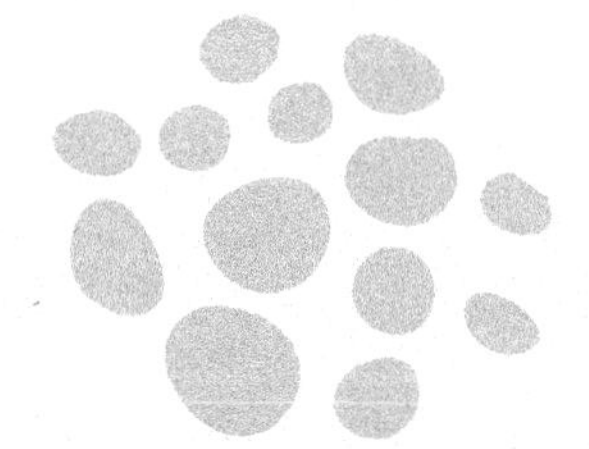

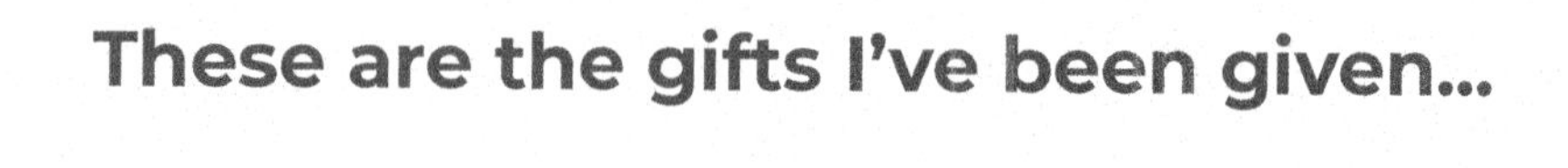

These are the gifts I've been given...

Things I love now...

(Date your entry and revisit it in the future.)

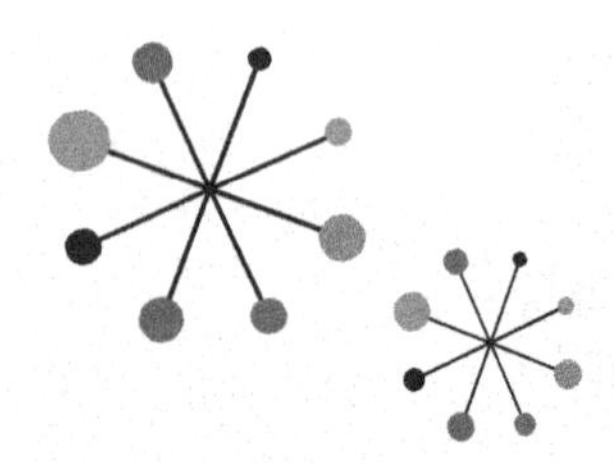

My shrine to all that I am obsessed with...

I could easily change...

you can DO IT

Friends I can always count on...

SAY

"I'M SORRY"

when

sorry is due

Sorry!

Apologies I owe...

it's okay

Places to go...

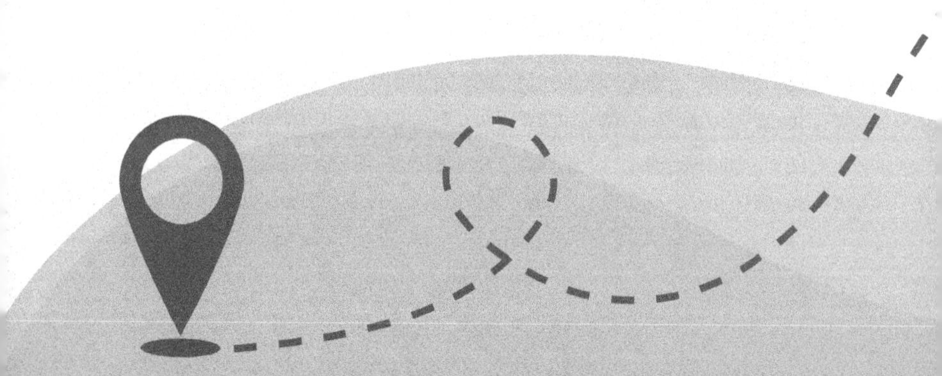

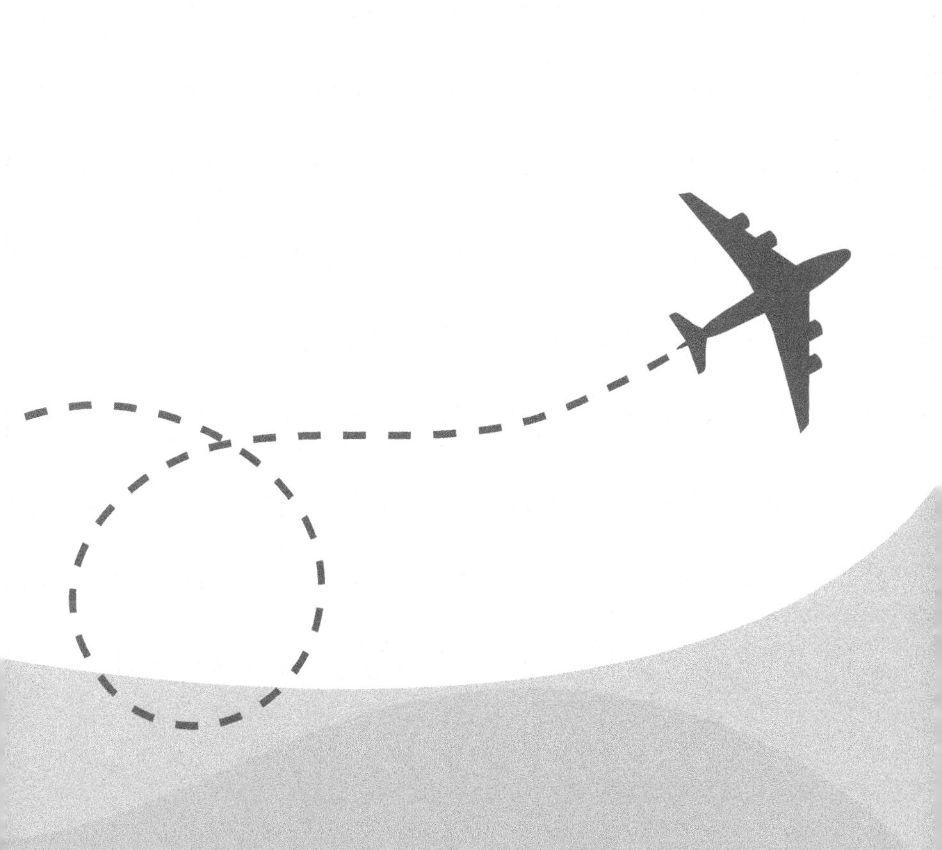

Things to do...

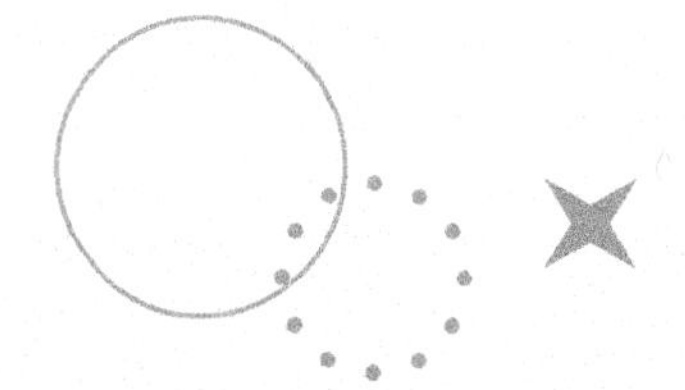

Beauty to see...

Turn Your camera OUTWARD

A poem for the world...

Comfort is...

Gentle reminders to myself...

ME

DON'T LET

someone else's

SUCCESS

stop you from

ACHIEVING

Your Own

My happiest place on earth is here...

My happiest place playlist...

What makes me sad...

START

EACH DAY

with

a moment

of GRATITUDE

My gratitude prayer...

Morning musings...

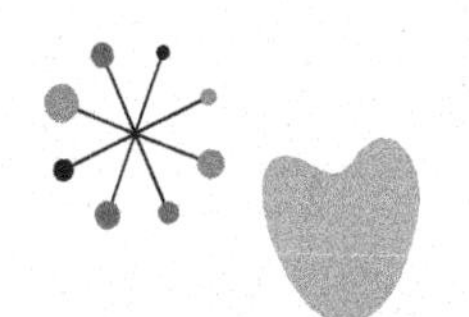

I had the weirdest dream...

That's Weird

This is my tribe...

When I was a kid, I...

When I am old, I will...

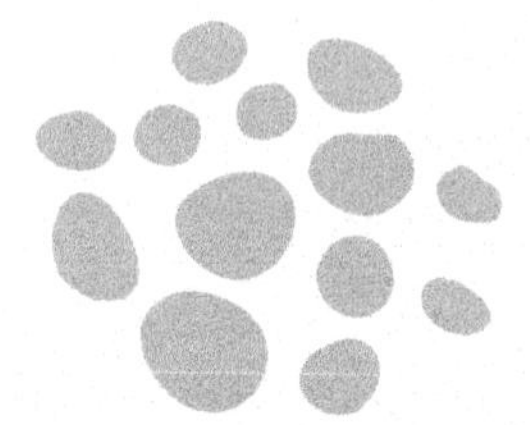

Things that stress me out...

NO
is Not
a
BAD
WORD

No!

No is a hard word to learn. Easy to spell, hard to practice.

Sometimes we really want to say no, but we don't want to hurt someone else's feelings.

So instead, we say yes, and end up hurting ourselves.

Practice saying no here.

Write it as many times as you can fit on this page.

Say it out loud as you write it.

Shout it as loud as you can!

YES

Now finish these sentences...

No, I won't

No, I can't

No, I don’t want to

No, I don’t like

No, I will never

Goals in sight...

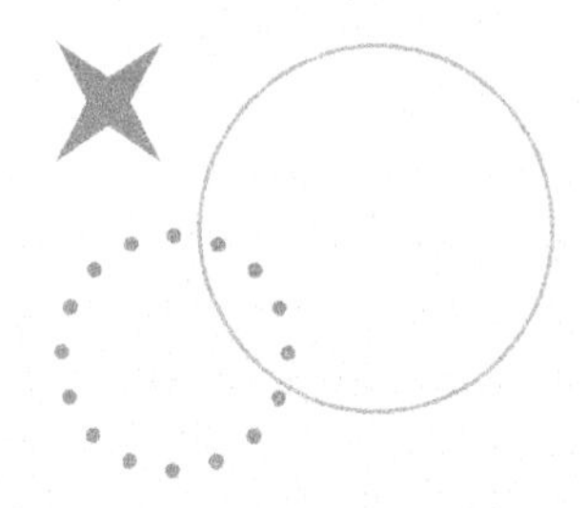

Monthly goals and musings

January

lets
do
this

My January goals & musings...

My February goals & musings...

Stay
POSITIVE

Today
is the
day

My March goals & musings...

My April goals & musings...

keep
GOING

don't
give
up

My May goals & musings...

My June goals & musings...

Spread
KiNDNESS

have a Good day

My July goals & musings...

My August goals & musings...

I BELiEVE
in You

POSITIVE
THOUGHTS

My September goals & musings...

My October goals & musings...

HANG
in
THERE

yes!!!

My November goals & musings...

My December goals & musings...

Good
Vibes
ONLY

My year in review...

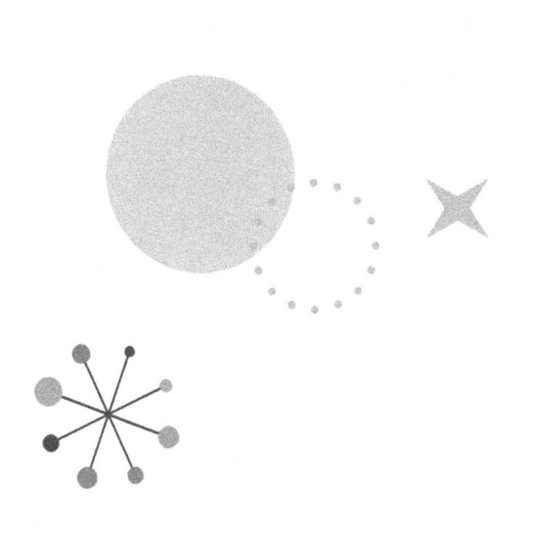

My big plans for next year...

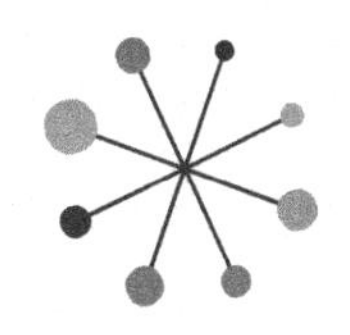

Do MORE
OF WHAT
MAKES ME
Happy

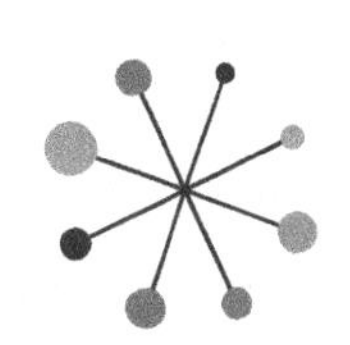

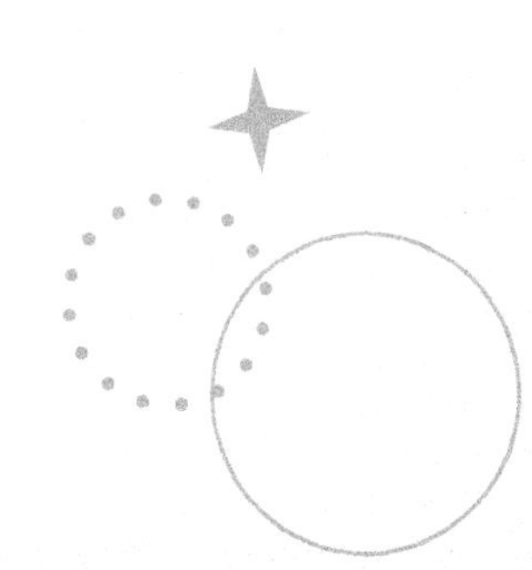

Be
Humble

Right now I’m totally in love with...

My crush today is...

Love

The first time I was in love it felt like...

My dream date would be...

We would go to...

I would wear...

The first time I had my heart broken it felt like...

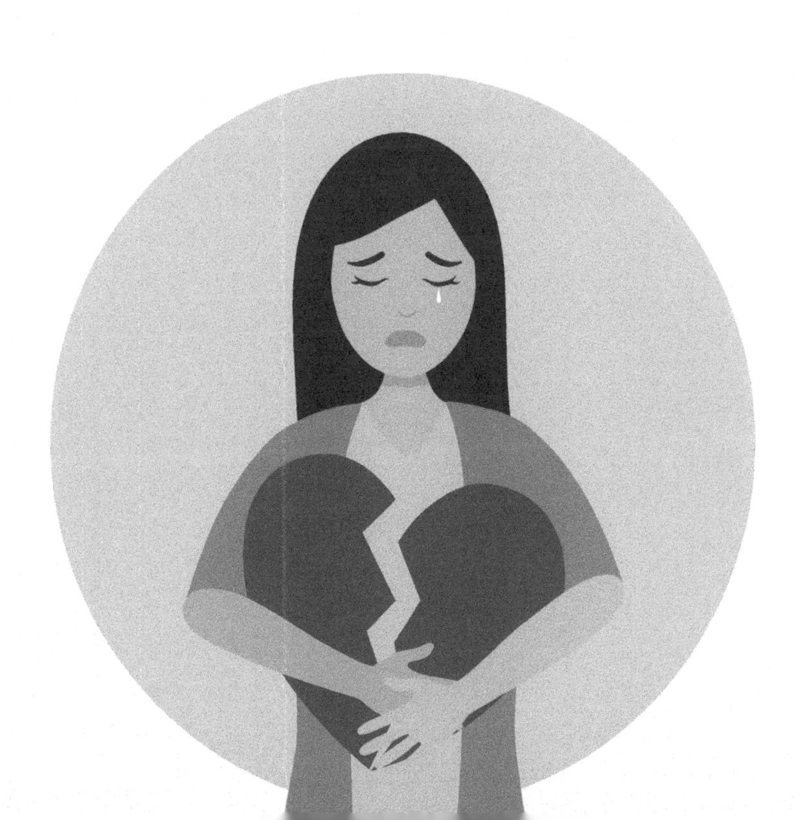

The first person who ever broke my heart...

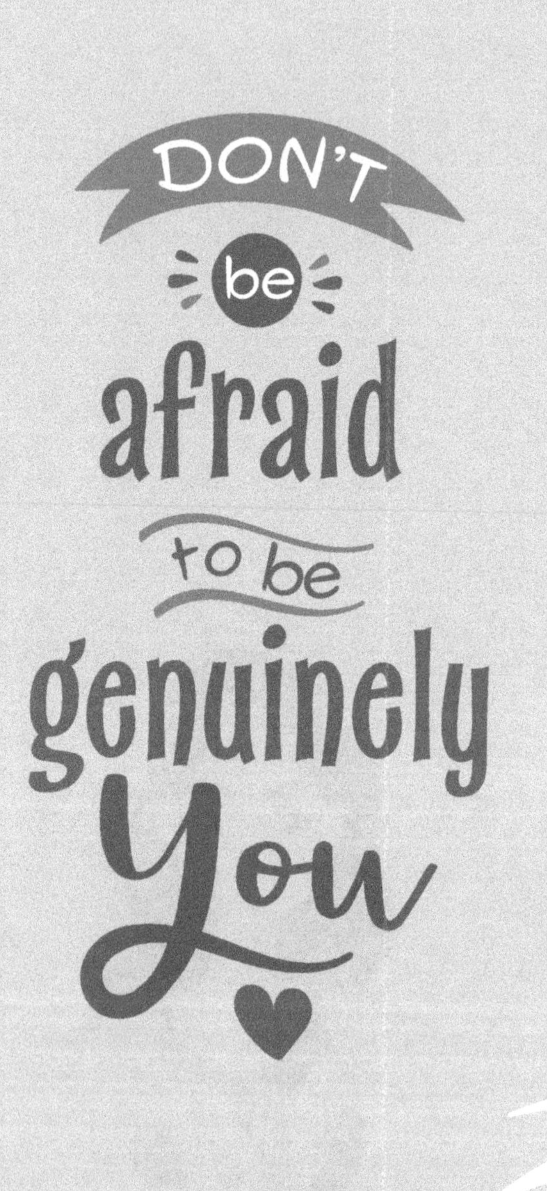
DON'T
be
afraid
to be
genuinely
You

My personal brand in 25 words...

The story of my life in hashtags...

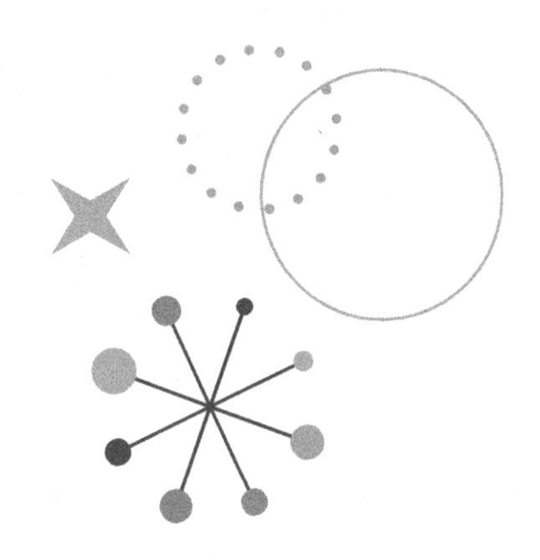

LOL
###
OMG))

5 x 7 x 5
Today in a haiku...

My signature meal is...

(Write it out like a recipe.)

Star light, star bright, the wish I wish tonight...

The biggest secret I’m keeping now...

ACCEPT
COMPLIMENTS
WITH
grace
and
thanks

I totally rock at...

How I can turn my rockin’ skills into a job one day...

My ultimate, fabulous dream job would be...

My dream job is ...

If I were an animal, I would be a...

A love poem about my favorite food...

THERE IS
nowhere
YOUR
MIND
can't
Take You!

This is how I plan to make a difference in the world...

My name in 25 different styles...

A drawing of my favorite flower...

(Draw a whole garden if you're feeling inspired!)

If I were in a movie, it would be...

and I would play...

because...

My ultimate concert would be...

At the...

(Dream big here!)

Draw your own VIP all access pass here...

WORRY LESS
about
WHAT PEOPLE
think of You
and
more about
what You think
of YOURSELF

Standing in front of a mirror, this is what I see...

The earliest memory I have is...

To respect me is to...

BEING FEARLESS DOESN'T mean you CAN'T EVER BE SCARED

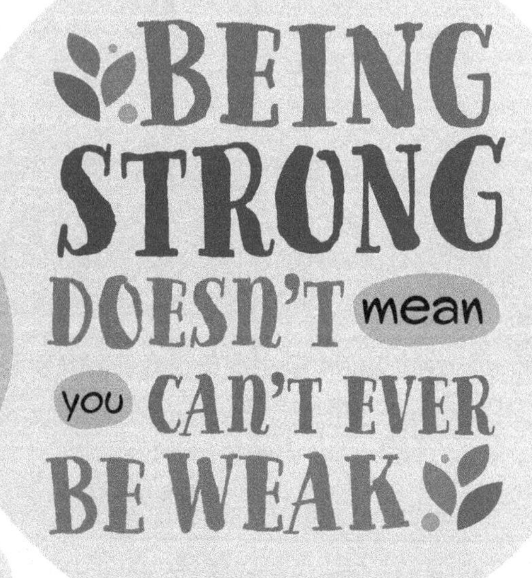

BEING HAPPY DOESN'T mean you CAN'T EVER BE SAD

What being fearless means to me...

no
fear
girl

What being strong means to me...

What being happy means to me...

Things I'm afraid of...

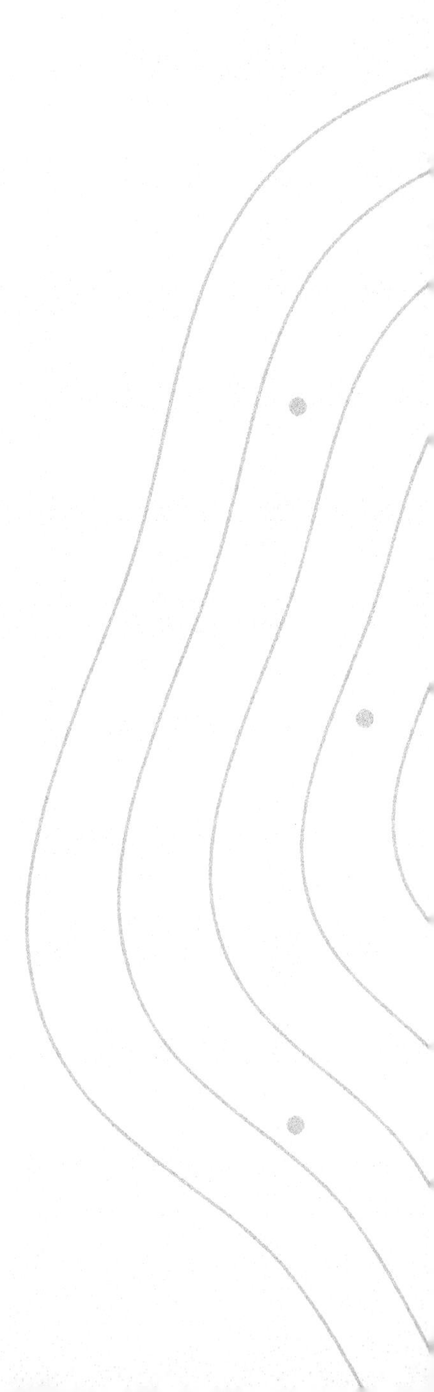

My top 10 greatest achievements to date...

What I hope to achieve in the future...

My 10 favorite quotes from 10 amazing women...
?
...

My favorite teacher is/was...

And this is what I learned from her/him/them...

My Favorite Teacher

Times I won and how it felt...

Times I lost and how it felt...

ADMIT
YOUR
Mistakes

MISTAKES
MEAN
You've Tried

Places I like to hang out...

OMG...my most embarrassing moment was when I...

NEVER

BE

Afraid

to ask

Questions

???

The first song I ever knew all the words to was...

(Write the song here!)

Five laws I'd put into action right now...

Things I believe in...

Things I don't believe in...

Issues worth fighting for...

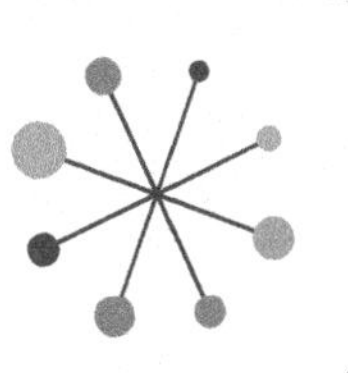

WE CAN DO IT

What freedom means to me...

My prayer for the world...

Write a 500 word essay on someone you admire...

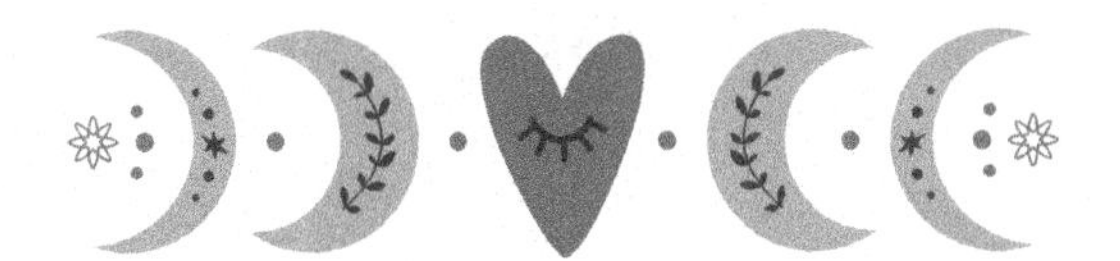

I ADMIRE YOU!

I

Believe

in

You

Made in USA - Kendallville, IN
81734_9781735445205
08.27.2022 1253